# Stimulus texts

In this section of the workbook you will be given examples of many different text types and asked first to analyse them individually, applying **language methods** and an understanding of **contextual factors**, and then to consider which groupings best suit the range of texts you have analysed.

Language methods are referred to in the AQA B specification as being made up of:

- **lexis:** words and their meanings (the latter are also referred to as **semantics** by many)
- **grammar:** structural relationships between words, phrases, clauses and utterances
- **phonology/phonetics:** the sounds of English and how they are employed
- **pragmatics:** the implied meanings of language choices, often dependent upon context and shared understanding
- **discourse:** both how texts 'stick together' as units and the devices used to structure them, and the ways in which language reflects and represents different strands of identity (for example, the discourse of a particular group of people in society, such as the police, military or medical profession)

- **graphology** [...] ges on the pag[...] gns, images and [...]

While it is important to use these language methods as part of your analysis and grouping of texts in Section A, it is wrong to think that everything you do should be based on labelling language features. Contexts and meanings are vital too and you should try to integrate all three AOs to achieve the best mark possible.

Each stimulus text comes with a set of questions that you need to answer in the spaces provided. These questions build up to become more detailed and demanding, until after several stimulus texts you get longer, more exam-style questions. With these longer questions, you will need to take a step back from the details of individual texts and start to think about the bigger picture.

When thinking of your responses to the short questions and the longer exam-style questions, it is a good idea to keep the mark scheme in mind. Below is a simplified version of the Section A mark scheme.

**Mark scheme for Section A**

| | AO1 (16 marks) Use of language methods/ clear communication | AO2 (16 marks) Range and discussion of grouping choices | AO3 (16 marks) Contextual awareness |
|---|---|---|---|
| Very good | Responses will be systematic and evaluative There will be accurate and perceptive use of language knowledge | Insight into choices of groups Well-chosen groups Intelligent and tentative reasons for choices Subtleties explored | Insight into how contexts influence meaning Analytical and systematic interpretation of texts and contexts Uses data to support interpretation |
| Sound—good | Responses will use some language methods, ranging up to systematic uses of methods There will be appropriate and accurate use of language knowledge | Responses will range from a number of groups up to a range of groups Sound responses will describe and analyse groups; good responses will offer more developed discussion Some grasp of complexity of groups | Awareness of context (sound) leading up to clear understanding (good) of context Understanding of links between language uses and contexts Supports interpretation with data |
| Undeveloped | Some attempts made to respond analytically, but unconvincing Needs to be developed with more detail and accuracy | Only limited number of groups Rather superficial Descriptive rather than analytical | Broad and general; in need of more detail and depth Limited links between language and context |
| Very weak | Very little evidence of methods being applied or knowledge being shown | Unhelpful or very basic groups Little grasp of how to use language methods to group texts | Summarises rather than analyses Superficial and generalised |

# Stimulus text A

Read Stimulus text A, which is a photograph of a notice about bicycles being chained to railings, and answer the following questions.

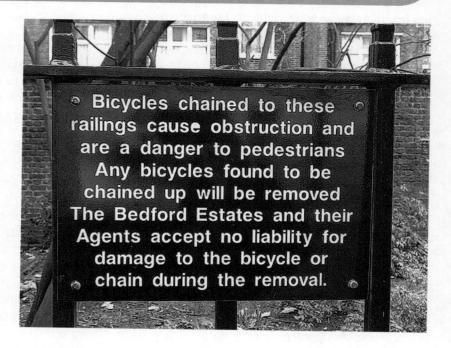

Bicycles chained to these railings cause obstruction and are a danger to pedestrians Any bicycles found to be chained up will be removed The Bedford Estates and their Agents accept no liability for damage to the bicycle or chain during the removal.

**1** **What are the main purposes of the language used in this text?**

**2** **How does the layout or *graphology* of the text assist with these purposes?**

**3** **What is the nature of the *register* of the language being adopted? What relationship is suggested between text producer and text audience?**

**4** **In what ways do the grammatical structures used in this text assist its purposes?**

# Stimulus text B

Read Stimulus text B, which is a leaflet promoting and explaining strike action against pension cuts for education workers, and answer the following questions.

---

**STOP THE GREAT PENSIONS ROBBERY**

30 November 2011

## Day of action to defend public sector pensions

- We are striking today alongside up to three million teachers, school leaders, support staff, civil servants, council staff and health workers.

- Our pensions are under attack from a government that wants us to pay more and work longer for a lot less.

- Please support our campaign for fair pensions.

www.ucu.org.uk

**STOP THE GREAT PENSIONS ROBBERY**

---

**5** Who do you think the intended audience of this text is?

.................................................................................................................

.................................................................................................................

**6** What effect does the graphology of this leaflet have in meeting the purposes of this text?

.................................................................................................................

.................................................................................................................

.................................................................................................................

**7** Do you notice any patterns to the lexical choices and semantic fields created in the text?

.................................................................................................................

.................................................................................................................

**8** How do the grammatical structures used in this poster fit with its possible purposes?

.................................................................................................................

.................................................................................................................

# Grouping stimulus texts A and B

One of the most important elements of your work on this unit is your ability to see how texts are connected and the groups that you can put them into. This can be based on the texts' audiences, purposes and/or design, but could also be related to the mode of the texts (whether they are spoken, written or somewhere in the middle) or their use of specific language or grammar features. Alternatively, it could be related to broader themes such as the texts' use of humour or images, or a shared standpoint. It is also possible to see connections in the themes and ideas represented in some texts and to create groupings based on these.

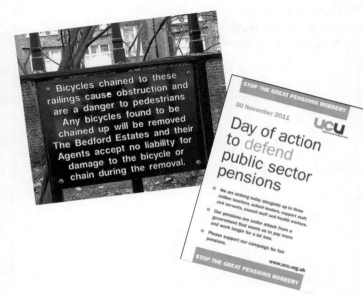

In the two examples you have looked at so far, the texts are clearly designed to fulfil a very definite set of purposes, but what similarities are there in the language used?

Think about the following questions to see if you can start making connections between the two texts you have looked at so far.

**9** How can you tell that each text is designed to place some kind of pressure on the intended audience? What language features can you spot that apply pressure to a reader?

..........................................................................................................................

..........................................................................................................................

..........................................................................................................................

..........................................................................................................................

..........................................................................................................................

..........................................................................................................................

..........................................................................................................................

**10** What could you say about the ways in which each text uses graphology to help support the meaning of the words? How is each text designed to make the message work?

..........................................................................................................................

..........................................................................................................................

..........................................................................................................................

..........................................................................................................................

# Stimulus text C

Stimulus text C is an extract from Nick Clegg's September 2011 speech to the Liberal Democrat Party's Annual Conference.

Liberal Democrats, we have now been in Government for 500 days. Not easy, is it? None of us thought it would be a walk in the park, but I suspect none of us predicted just how tough it would turn out to be. We 've lost support, we 've lost councillors, and we lost a referendum. I know how painful it has been to face anger and frustration on the doorstep.

Some of you may have even wondered: Will it all be worth it in the end? It will be. And today I want to explain why.

But above all I want to pay tribute to you. Your resilience. Your grace under fire. I have been genuinely moved by your spirit and your strength. Thank you. Thank you, above all, for never forgetting what we are in politics for. After the May elections, Alex Cole-Hamilton, one of our defeated candidates in Edinburgh, said that if losing was part payment for ending child detention then, as he said: 'I accept it, with all my heart.'

That is the liberal spirit and that is something we will never lose. The spirit that gave birth to our party a century and a half ago, that kept us alive when the other two parties tried to kill us off. The spirit that means however great our past, our fight will always be for a better future.

Down in Westminster we've been vilified like never before. The Left and the Right didn't like us much in opposition. They like us a whole lot less in Government. The Left accuse us of being powerless puppets, duped by a right wing Conservative clique.

The Right accuse us of being a sinister left wing clique, who've duped powerless Conservatives. I do wish they'd make up their mind.

So yes, it has been hard. And adversity tests the character of a party just as it tests any person. We've shown — you've shown — immense strength. After being hit hard, we picked ourselves up and we came out fighting. Fighting to keep the NHS safe. Fighting to protect human rights. Fighting to create jobs. Fighting for every family. Not doing the easy thing, but doing the right thing. Not easy, but right.

And as for all those seats we lost in May, let me tell you this: I won't rest, we won't rest, until we've won every single one of those seats back.

**11** What kinds of sentence functions are used in these two extracts and why do you think Clegg has included them?

...................................................................................................................................

...................................................................................................................................

**12** What kinds of words are these and what kind of effect do you think they might be designed to have?

...................................................................................................................................

...................................................................................................................................

**13** What techniques does Nick Clegg employ in these paragraphs and what do you think his desired effect might be?

...................................................................................................................................

...................................................................................................................................

...................................................................................................................................

...................................................................................................................................

# Stimulus text D

Stimulus text D is an extract from a *Choose Your Own Adventure* gamebook, set in a distant universe, in which you make the choices to decide what happens to your character.

Your battleship approaches the alien planet and takes up orbit position. Your scanners reveal that the planet appears to be inhabited and there are large areas of what might be urban habitation, as well as oceans of water. Your scanners also reveal that the atmosphere is very similar to that of Earth, with very few toxic elements present. However, radiation levels are very high and emanate from several huge craters that dot the landscape of the planet.

You try to make contact with sentient life forms through the ship's radio and hyperlink, but there appears to be little evidence of life. Just as you are about to give up, a signal is picked up by your systems assistant. She tells you that some life forms have been detected in an area towards the north pole of the planet and that they are issuing what appears to be a distress signal on a recognised frequency.

Will you beam down to this area and investigate the source of the signals (turn to 232), continue scanning the planet for resources you can take (turn to 412) or launch a salvo from your ship's cannons to obliterate the last remaining life forms (turn to 17)?

**14** **What kinds of pronouns and possessive determiners are used here? How do they relate to the reader?**

...................................................................................................................................................................

...................................................................................................................................................................

...................................................................................................................................................................

**15** **What tense is used with these verbs and verb phrases? How do they help achieve effects in the text?**

...................................................................................................................................................................

...................................................................................................................................................................

...................................................................................................................................................................

**16** **What sentence functions are used in the final paragraph and how do they relate to the nature of the text?**

...................................................................................................................................................................

...................................................................................................................................................................

...................................................................................................................................................................

**17** **What examples of descriptive language can you identify in this text and what kinds of word classes and structures are used to describe? How do these relate to the type of text and its purpose?**

...................................................................................................................................................................

...................................................................................................................................................................

...................................................................................................................................................................

...................................................................................................................................................................

# Stimulus text E

Stimulus text E is taken from the particulars of a house advertised for sale by an estate agent in London.

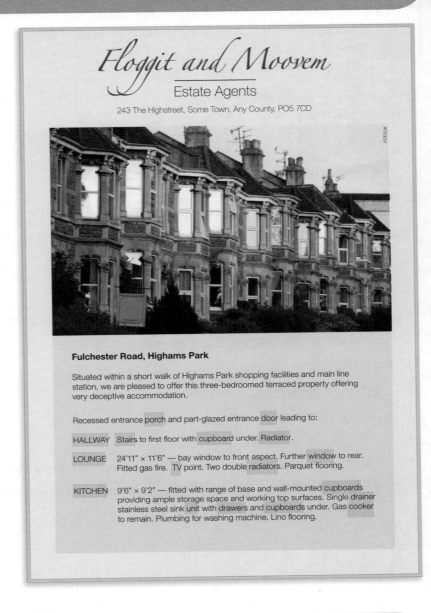

*Floggit and Moovem*
Estate Agents

243 The Highstreet, Some Town, Any County, PO5 7CD

**Fulchester Road, Highams Park**

Situated within a short walk of Highams Park shopping facilities and main line station, we are pleased to offer this three-bedroomed terraced property offering very deceptive accommodation.

Recessed entrance porch and part-glazed entrance door leading to:

HALLWAY    Stairs to first floor with cupboard under. Radiator.

LOUNGE    24'11" × 11'6" — bay window to front aspect. Further window to rear. Fitted gas fire. TV point. Two double radiators. Parquet flooring.

KITCHEN    9'6" × 9'2" — fitted with range of base and wall-mounted cupboards providing ample storage space and working top surfaces. Single drainer stainless steel sink unit with drawers and cupboards under. Gas cooker to remain. Plumbing for washing machine. Lino flooring.

**18** **All of the highlighted words belong to one word class. Which is it and why is this important to the text?**

..................................................................................................................................

**19** **What do you think is the purpose of a text like this and how does this text achieve its purpose?**

..................................................................................................................................

..................................................................................................................................

..................................................................................................................................

..................................................................................................................................

# Stimulus text F

This text is an extract of a transcript of a conversation between two 9-year-old boys playing a game together on an Xbox 360 console.

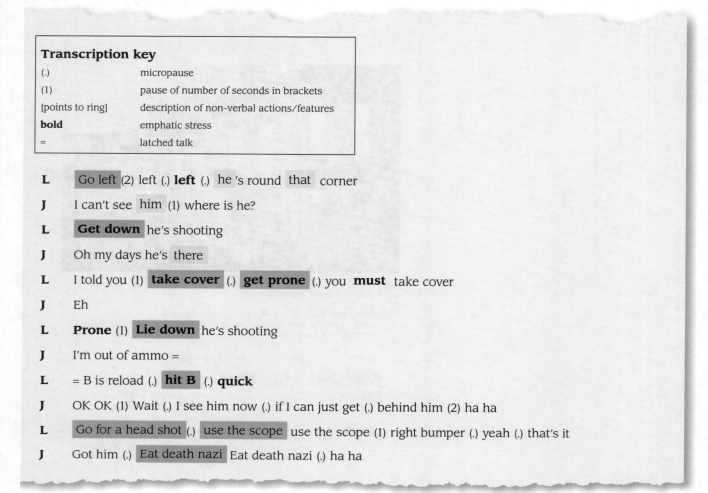

**Transcription key**

| | |
|---|---|
| (.) | micropause |
| (1) | pause of number of seconds in brackets |
| [points to ring] | description of non-verbal actions/features |
| **bold** | emphatic stress |
| = | latched talk |

**L**   Go left (2) left (.) **left** (.) he 's round that corner

**J**   I can't see him (1) where is he?

**L**   **Get down** he's shooting

**J**   Oh my days he's there

**L**   I told you (1) **take cover** (.) **get prone** (.) you **must** take cover

**J**   Eh

**L**   **Prone** (1) **Lie down** he's shooting

**J**   I'm out of ammo =

**L**   = B is reload (.) **hit B** (.) **quick**

**J**   OK OK (1) Wait (.) I see him now (.) if I can just get (.) behind him (2) ha ha

**L**   Go for a head shot (.) use the scope use the scope (1) right bumper (.) yeah (.) that's it

**J**   Got him (.) Eat death nazi Eat death nazi (.) ha ha

---

**20**   **What connects the significance of the highlighted words here? How are they important to what is going on in the transcript?**

.................................................................................................................................................

.................................................................................................................................................

**21**   **What sentence function is being used in the highlighted extracts and why is it important to the nature of this conversation and the relationship between the two speakers?**

.................................................................................................................................................

.................................................................................................................................................

.................................................................................................................................................

.................................................................................................................................................

# Stimulus text G

This text is an extract of a transcript of a chef explaining how to cook a vegetarian meal.

**Transcription key**

| | |
|---|---|
| (.) | micropause |
| (1) | pause of number of seconds in brackets |
| [points to ring] | description of non-verbal actions |
| **bold** | emphatic stress |
| = | latched talk |

This meal is just perfect for those in your family who like a bit of **spice** (.) it's a really simple dish to cook and uses fairly easy-to-source ingredients (.) sooo I've got some garlic here (1) into the pan it goes(.) need a bit of oil (2) roughly chop up some red onions too and bung them in (1) now while that's lightly frying we can cut up the red chilli (1) slice it nice and thin (2) I leave the seeds in as I like a bit of extra heat (.) and I always like to add just a few sprinkles of chipotle chilli flakes for a warmer glow (1) but if you are a chilli fan then add some habanero chilli or even some birds eye chillis (.) it's up to you (2) I love chipotle (.) such a lovely flavour (1) now it's time to add the veggie balls (.) I always make my own with sosmix and egg but I know other people quite like quorn balls (.) so I make sure they've got just a dusting of paprika so that when they fry they seal in some of that spice (1) mmm (.) making me hungry just thinking about it now (2) OK so while all of that is frying I'll get two tins of chopped tomatoes (.) a spoonful or two (.) or three (.) of sundried tomato paste (1) there we go (.) add it all to the pan and stir (.) aaand let it all simmer nicely for a good twenty minutes (1) now for the flatbreads

22. **What connects the highlighted words or phrases here? How are they important to what is going on in the transcript?**

23. **Why are the highlighted words important in this transcript?**

24. **What kinds of pronouns are highlighted here and how are they significant to what is going on in this transcript?**

13

# Stimulus text H

This text is an extract of an online discussion on a music forum between five posters discussing an album by Snow Patrol.

**Post subject: Snow Patrol new album Fallen Empires. Does anyone care?**    6.02am
Widget (veteran)
So...has anyone listened to it yet?

**Post subject: Snow Patrol new album Fallen Empires. Does anyone care?**    6.03am
Hannah G (noob)
meh

**Post subject: Snow Patrol new album Fallen Empires. Does anyone care?**    6.06am
Biscuit Tin Maestro (veteran)
Next question

**Post subject: Snow Patrol new album Fallen Empires. Does anyone care?**    6.07am
Das Winkleshiner (novice)
won't listen to them agin after the last album. proper grim

**Post subject: Snow Patrol new album Fallen Empires. Does anyone care?**    6.07am
Widget (veteran)
is ok...growing on me a bit now. Def better than last 2 albums and 2 or 3 standout trax on it. but what do i know, i thought last friendly fires was good 😊

**Post subject: Snow Patrol new album Fallen Empires. Does anyone care?**    6.09am
Hannah G (noob)
double meh

**Post subject: Snow Patrol new album Fallen Empires. Does anyone care?**    6.11am
Widget (veteran)
do you know any other words

**Post subject: Snow Patrol new album Fallen Empires. Does anyone care?**    6.14am
Hannah G (noob)
meh meh LOL and meh :o)

**Post subject: Snow Patrol new album Fallen Empires. Does anyone care?**    6.16am
BillyBob Bobby (supreme overlord)
It's got some sublime moments on it. 'Called Out in the Dark' and 'This Isn't Everything You Are' do it for me — beautiful songs

**Post subject: Snow Patrol new album Fallen Empires. Does anyone care?**    6.18am
Widget (veteran)
Thankyou an intelligent response at last

**Post subject: Snow Patrol new album Fallen Empires. Does anyone care?**    6.19am
Hannah G (noob)
meh

---

**25**   **What connects the highlighted words and why are they significant in this type of text?**

........................................................................................................................................

........................................................................................................................................

**26**   **Identify examples of interaction in this text. How is the interaction in a computer-mediated communication (CMC) text like this different from that in a spoken text?**

........................................................................................................................................

........................................................................................................................................

........................................................................................................................................

........................................................................................................................................

........................................................................................................................................

........................................................................................................................................

........................................................................................................................................

# Grouping the texts

Which groups would you place Stimulus texts A–H in and why? Write in the spaces provided.

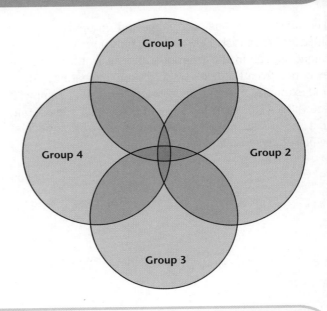

**27** **Group 1 What grouping is this?**

.............................................................................................

**Which texts are part of it?**

.............................................................................................

.............................................................................................

**Group 2 What grouping is this?**

.............................................................................................

**Which texts are part of it?**

.............................................................................................

**Group 3 What grouping is this?**

.............................................................................................

**Which texts are part of it?**

.............................................................................................

.............................................................................................

**Group 4 What grouping is this?**

.............................................................................................

**Which texts are part of it?**

.............................................................................................

.............................................................................................

# Suggested groupings

The table below has four suggested groupings already filled in. Your task here is to think about which texts might appear in these groups and fill in the language evidence from the texts by selecting key features, ideas and examples from the appropriate texts. For example, if you think that Group 1 — spoken texts — should contain text F, choose an appropriate extract from that text which shows that it is spoken.

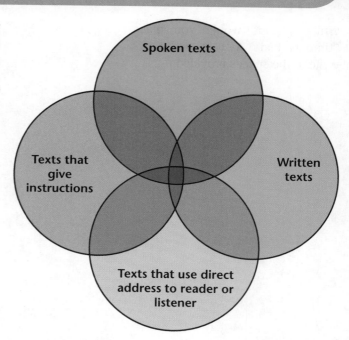

| **Group 1: spoken texts**<br>Linguistic and contextual evidence and examples | **Group 2: written texts**<br>Linguistic and contextual evidence and examples |
|---|---|
| **Group 3: texts that use direct address to reader or listener**<br>Linguistic and contextual evidence and examples | **Group 4: texts that give instructions**<br>Linguistic and contextual evidence and examples |

You have already answered several questions on Stimulus texts A–H, identifying key features of language, audience, purpose and topic, which will help you with your groupings, but it is also worth thinking back through all the texts and identifying specific features that can be linked to the suggested groupings above.

**28** **Identify two or three examples of the following:**

**a** **direct address in texts A, C, D, F, G and H**

.................................................................................................................................

.................................................................................................................................

.................................................................................................................................

.................................................................................................................................

.................................................................................................................................

.................................................................................................................................

.................................................................................................................................

**b** **instructions in texts A, F and G**

.................................................................................................................................

.................................................................................................................................

.................................................................................................................................

.................................................................................................................................

.................................................................................................................................

.................................................................................................................................

.................................................................................................................................

**c** **features of interaction between participants in texts F and H**

.................................................................................................................................

.................................................................................................................................

.................................................................................................................................

.................................................................................................................................

.................................................................................................................................

.................................................................................................................................

.................................................................................................................................

Remember that you can have texts that appear more than once across different groups and that examiners are often keen to see you show awareness of how one text shows a range of different features that might help it appear in two or more groups at once.

Text F, for example, could appear in four groups (spoken mode, direct address, instruction and interaction), but you might decide to choose separate parts or language details of that text to illustrate why it is in one group. For instance, you might decide that one of the language features that marks out text F as spoken is its use of ellipsis (a common feature in spontaneous conversations — spoken or through computer-mediated communication (CMC) — where grammatical elements are left out because they are already clear from the context), while it also qualifies for the group of instruction texts because of its use of imperative verb forms and modal auxiliaries (both of which would need to be exemplified in your answer to convince the examiner you know what they are and can spot them in the text).

Another point worth remembering is that while you can group texts together, there are likely to be variations between the texts within a group. The texts that are offering instruction, for example, might do it in very different ways — some very direct, others less obvious. Examiners are keen to reward candidates who show a more subtle awareness of variation within groups too.

Take texts A, F and G, for example. Text A is direct and forceful, using straightforward imperative verb forms. Text G is more casual and friendly in its register, telling the audience how to create the meal but using mitigated directives (softened or less direct means of offering instruction, such as 'aaand let it all simmer nicely') or using the first person to describe how she is doing it as a means of instructing the viewer (e.g. 'so I make sure they've got just a dusting of paprika') and friendly asides, which comes across as less abrupt and threatening. Text F involves one boy giving the other quite detailed and urgent instructions about how to play the Xbox game, and so is very dependent on context. You would expect it to be urgent and forceful, because his intended audience (the other boy) needs to make snap decisions and react quickly. All three texts offer instruction, but do it in very different ways.

Now you have looked at your first eight texts and thought about how you might group them, it is time to answer the following question yourself.

---

**29** **Discuss various ways in which texts A–H can be grouped, giving linguistic reasons for your choices.**

48 marks

**Plan the key points of your answer to this exam-style question in the space provided here before writing your answer on separate sheets of paper.**

..............................................................................................................................
..............................................................................................................................
..............................................................................................................................
..............................................................................................................................
..............................................................................................................................
..............................................................................................................................
..............................................................................................................................
..............................................................................................................................
..............................................................................................................................
..............................................................................................................................
..............................................................................................................................
..............................................................................................................................
..............................................................................................................................

# Further texts

Over the next few pages you will find a further eight texts, similar to those you have already looked at. Study the texts I–P. These texts illustrate different varieties of language use. This time round, you will not be asked questions on each separate text, but asked an exam-style question at the end (on pages 26–27).

# Stimulus text I

### Extract from Alexis Petridis's *Guardian* review of Cher Lloyd's album

Certainly, the feeling that her people don't really have a clue what to do with Cher Lloyd permeates Sticks + Stones. They try pretty much everything, from Lily Allenisms on Over the Moon to post-Umbrella R&B balladry on End Up Here. Grow Up drafts in Busta Rhymes for some Black Eyed Peasish video-game hip-hop so tinny that a listener of a certain age will think not of will.i.am but Jet Set Willy. Beautiful People is a sub-Linda Perry self-help power ballad. Dub on the Track borrows its pop-dubstep dynamic — and indeed melody — from Katy B's Katy On a Mission, which if nothing else is an improvement on borrowing the melody from Oh My Darling Clementine — known to many primarily as Huckleberry Hound's favourite song — as Lloyd's debut single Swagger Jagger did. Playa Boi tries to update Neneh Cherry's Buffalo Stance, which is probably necessary — there would be something a bit weird about an 18-year-old covering a song about a mid-80s fashion movement in 2011 — but it loses the original's idiosyncratic charm amid a wash of generic synths and lyrical references to players and gangsters.

Cher Lloyd

TopFoto

*Copyright Guardian News & Media Ltd 2011* **http://www.guardian. co.uk/music/2011/nov/03/cher-lloyd-sticks-and-stones-review**

# Stimulus text J

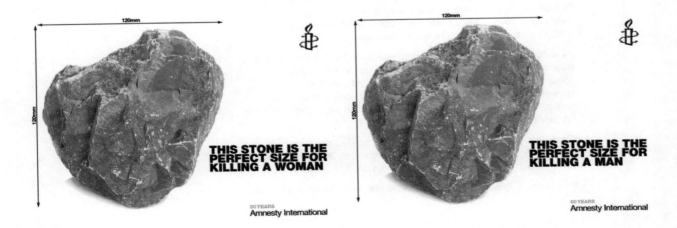

*Reproduced by permission of Amnesty International UK/Different Kettle*

# IN IRAN, STONING A PERSON TO DEATH IS NOT AGAINST THE LAW. USING THE WRONG STONE IS.

**As you read these words, at least 14 people in Iran are at risk of execution by stoning.**

Bound, wrapped in shrouds and buried in a pit with head and shoulders above ground, the victims are likely to survive for between 20 minutes and two hours from when the first stone thrown draws blood. The reason they survive so long can be found in the chillingly clinical wording of Article 104 of the Iranian Penal Code:

*'The size of the stone used in stoning shall not be too large to kill the convict by one or two throws and at the same time shall not be too small to be called a stone.'*

**By supporting Amnesty now, you can help get stoning outlawed in Iran forever.**

Many Iranians are opposed to stoning and courageous activists such as Asieh Amini have been harassed, persecuted and, for their own safety, forced to live in exile. Those people – and the ten women and four men who face death by stoning – need your support now.

**Right now, we have a unique opportunity to stop the stoning.**

Amnesty International knows that Iranian authorities are currently reviewing the country's Penal Code. We're convinced that if enough people like you stand up to be counted, Iran will finally bow to our long-standing campaign and ban execution by stoning.

**How you can help.**

You can become an Amnesty supporter now by making a regular gift of £2 a month. Your money will help us to lobby the Iranian authorities to comply with international law. It will support our research to identify people sentenced to death by stoning so that we can campaign on their behalf. And your money will also help us to raise public awareness, build outrage against this abhorrent practice and encourage supporters to take action themselves.

By supporting us, you can make it crystal clear that the stoning has to stop once and for all – because millions of us say so. Together, we speak with one voice in defence of human rights; leaders, governments and corporations all listen. So if you believe this is wrong, join us. The more of us who stand up and say 'Stop', the more influence we have. It's really that simple.

Please make sure when you return your completed donation form that you also sign and return the action card enclosed. By doing so, you will add to the pressure we apply to Iranian decision makers.

Please grasp this opportunity to end the obscenity of stoning forever.

*Asieh Amini is a journalist and poet. Her report of a stoning in Iran shocked many who had been led to believe the practice had been abandoned. In the face of constant harassment she has been driven into exile.*

*Reproduced by permission of Amnesty International UK/Different Kettle*

# Stimulus text K

Text K is a transcript of an advertisement by the British Heart Foundation for 'Hands-only CPR', featuring the footballer and actor Vinnie Jones.

**Transcription key**

| | |
|---|---|
| (.) | micropause |
| (1) | pause of number of seconds in brackets |
| [points to ring] | description of non-verbal actions |
| **bold** | emphatic stress |
| = | latched talk |

[Vinnie Jones enters with two burly associates]

My name is Vinnie Jones and I'm gonna teach you a lesson you'll never forget (1) there are times in life when bein' tough comes in 'andy (1) say some geezer collapses in front of you (.) what do you do (.) we need a volunteer that ain't breathin' (3)

[burly associates slide unconscious man along floor towards Vinnie]

'ere's one I made earlier

[music 'Staying Alive' by the Bee Gees begins]

first thing you do is you check 'im over (1) if he ain't responsive or he ain't breathin' (.) or he's making noises like this [unconscious man makes a noise] then 'is 'eart's stopped and he's havin' a cardiac arrest (1) look lively (.) first dial 999 (.) then you do hands-only CPR (.) and **no** kissin' (1) you only kiss your missus on the lips (.) **watch** (.) lock your fingers together (.) knuckles up (.) then push down (.) **right** on the sovereign [points to sovereign ring necklace on man and demonstrates technique in time to the music while associates start to dance awkwardly in background]

[louder] push down 5 or 6 centimetres (.) that's about 2 inches in old money (1) push hard and fast about 2 times a second (.) like to the beat of Stayin' Alive (1) worried you'll 'urt 'im (.) better a cracked rib than 'im kicking the bucket (2) keep this up till the ambulance arrives (1) so don't **forget** (.) check 'im over (.) call 999 push hard and fast to Stayin' Alive (.) it works (.) hands-only CPR (.) it ain't as hard as it looks

*Reproduced by permission of the British Heart Foundation*

This text is an example of a seven-year-old child's writing for school, describing what he did at the weekend.

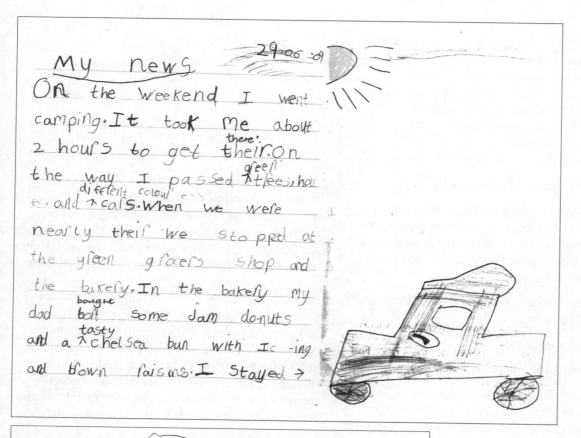

My news                    29·06·09

On the weekend I went
camping. It took me about
2 hours to get their. On
the way I passed ^green trees, hal
es. and ^cals. When we were
nearly their we stopped at
the green gracers shop and
the bakery. In the bakery my
dad bolt some jam do-nuts
and a ^tasty chelsea bun with ic -ing
and brown raisins. I stayed →

Page 2

there for 1 night and 2 day.
When I got there I climbed
the tree there. At lunch time
I only had 1 bite of
a sand wich and 1 whole jam
do-nut then my cosons came
and we played together for
the whole time. ✓

Well done fr using more interesting words
this week, Stanley! It sounds like you had
fun with your cousins!

*Reproduced with thanks to Stanley Clayton.*

# Stimulus text M

This text is an image of a sign by a recycling centre in London.

# Stimulus text N

This text is an extract of a script from a stand-up comedy show.

So, I thought, what's the best way to do a parody of observational comedy? And the best way to do a parody of observational comedy, I thought, was to do it from the point of view of an insect, about being an insect, whilst dressed as an insect, right. So, I'm an insect comedian, right, it'd be like this. I'm an insect, yeah?

[sniffs] 'Right, who's er, who's killed a grasshopper? Come on, we've all done it, haven't we? Friday night, we've all done it. There's a bloke down there laughing, he's on film and he's done it. And um…We've all done it, Friday night, killed a grasshopper, you get 'em don't you, in your mandibles, yeah, and er — not what you were thinking, mandibles, yeah, what are you thinking, what are you thinking — you get 'em and you spit your enzymes onto 'em, don't you, yeah, your enzymes, yeah, you spit your enzymes on 'em, on the grasshoppers…

Extract from *How I Escaped My Certain Fate*, Faber and Faber, p. 280.

*Reproduced by permission of Faber and Faber*

**Stewart Lee**

This text is taken from a fire evacuation procedures sign in a public building.

# Fire evacuation procedure

**If you discover a fire**

1   Raise the alarm, activate alarm call point
2   Dial 2222, inform security of fire location
3   Assist in the evacuation of the public
    and leave by the nearest safe exit

If safe to do so, attempt to extinguish the fire using the correct fire equipment. Do not take risks. Maintain a safe exit

**On hearing the alarm**

1   Calmly assist in evacuating the public
2   Leave the building by the nearest safe exit
3   Once outside proceed to the assembly point
    at the staff entrance

**Do not use the lifts**
**Do not re-enter the building**

# Stimulus text P

This text is taken from the website of an indie music club explaining its music policy.

---

**HOW DOES IT FEEL TO BE LOVED?**

**Music Policy**

Hello!

I just wanted to briefly explain the music policy of the club and introduce you to the nebulous concept known as "the remit".

HDIF is - broadly - a club that plays indie and soul. The Smiths to The Supremes, as we say on the board outside the Buffalo Bar. But that doesn't mean that we play all indie and all soul. We favour indie pop rather than indie rock - and the soul originates chiefly from the sixties rather than the seventies. I find it hard to offer any logical explanation for this, other than (a) it feels right and (b) has something to do with the rich vein of pop that runs through both. I've never been too sure what the term "rockist" means, but rest assured HDIF is defiantly and decidedly unrockist. We love pop, we love guitars that jangle, we love footstomping melodies and huge choruses.

Here's a list of musical types we don't play:

No punk; No rock; No metal; No grunge; No Britpop; No american college rock/indie rock; No contemporary haircut indie; No dance music;  No hip hop No shoegazing;

Which kind of translates to:

Indie pop; Tamla Motown; Northern soul; French pop; Girl groups; Sixties heartbreak and so on

Our guest DJs are asked to re-interpret the remit in their own individual way - ie, to stay true to the spirit of the club but to play whatever they want. Some DJs trash the rules completely, others bend them gently. You - and I - never know until the night itself. It's all part of the fun.

Most importantly of all, please come up and ask for requests. The best nights are when I'm just putting on a stream of excellent suggestions and the club pretty much DJs itself. And don't worry about hitting the remit spot on. No point in having rules if you don't break them every so often...!

---

*Reproduced by permission of Ian Watson and How Does It Feel To Be Loved?* (http://www.howdoesitfeel.co.uk/)

# Exam-style question

Here is an example of an exam question:

**01** Discuss various ways in which texts I–P can be grouped, giving linguistic reasons for your choices.

To help you answer this question, look at the feedback from the first eight texts (A–H) that you have studied and analysed and then try the following.

Group the texts using the template below, filling in linguistic and contextual reasons for your choices, as suggested.

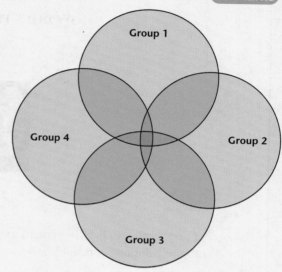

- Write your answer in the space provided.
- Check the feedback given for this question online.
- Look at the extracts of sample student answers on page 28 and see how you would rate these.

**Group 1** What grouping is this?

..................................................................................

**Which texts are part of it?**

..................................................................................

..................................................................................

..................................................................................

**Group 2** What grouping is this?

..................................................................................

**Which texts are part of it?**

..................................................................................

..................................................................................

..................................................................................

**Group 3** What grouping is this?

..................................................................................

**Which texts are part of it?**

..................................................................................

..................................................................................

**Group 4** What grouping is this?

..................................................................................

**Which texts are part of it?**

..................................................................................

..................................................................................

..................................................................................

| Group 1
Linguistic and contextual evidence and examples | Group 3
Linguistic and contextual evidence and examples |
| --- | --- |
| Group 2
Linguistic and contextual evidence and examples | Group 4
Linguistic and contextual evidence and examples |

**Plan the key points of your answer to the exam-type question in the space provided here before writing your answer on separate sheets of paper.**

......................................................................................................................................................
......................................................................................................................................................
......................................................................................................................................................
......................................................................................................................................................
......................................................................................................................................................
......................................................................................................................................................
......................................................................................................................................................
......................................................................................................................................................
......................................................................................................................................................
......................................................................................................................................................
......................................................................................................................................................

## Example answer extracts

Here are two short extracts taken from student responses to the exam-type question on pages 26–27. How successful do you think these answers are? Which areas have the candidates done well on and which could be improved for each extract? Fill in your ideas in the spaces provided, referring to the simplified AQA mark scheme (on page 5).

You can find more detailed feedback on each of these responses in the online answers.

### Extract 1

The first group I will discuss is texts that use descriptive language. Text I is a good example of a written review which is designed to describe the writer's views about the music of Cher Lloyd. In the review the writer uses a lot of noun phrases to refer to the type of music she produces and what she is influenced by, and he decides that her music is not very good. Another text which uses descriptive language is text P and here the writer describes different types of music that are played at the club. Again many noun phrases are used and the language is specific to people who know about music. Text J uses descriptive language for different purposes, representing the Iranian regime in a negative way and the campaigners and activists as 'courageous' for example.

**What are the strengths of this extract?**

.........................................................................................................................................................

.........................................................................................................................................................

**What are the weaknesses or areas for improvement in this extract?**

.........................................................................................................................................................

.........................................................................................................................................................

.........................................................................................................................................................

### Extract 2

One of the groups I will look at is texts that use images alongside words, a group which includes texts J, K, L, M and P. Text M uses graphology as part of its overall purpose of explaining which items can be recycled. For example, the images of food and drink cans go with the words 'food, drink and aerosol cans'. A similar tactic is used with text P where the club promoter uses a picture of people dancing at the club to suggest that this is the type of happy atmosphere that will be present if you attend. It also gives strong clues about who the text is aimed at, and this is supported by the types of bands and artists mentioned (the proper nouns *Britpop* and *The Smiths* are two examples).

**What are the strengths of this extract?**

.........................................................................................................................................................

.........................................................................................................................................................

**What are the weaknesses or areas for improvement in this extract?**

.........................................................................................................................................................

.........................................................................................................................................................

# Section B
# Language and social contexts

The second section of the ENGB1 paper consists of questions on three topic areas:

- language and gender
- language and power
- language and technology

You are expected to answer one question from a choice of three — most centres will teach at least two of the topic areas. Be careful to choose a topic that you have studied, rather than a completely new one: however attractive the question may appear, it is likely that you will do much better if you attempt a question that you have been prepared for.

The approach needed for Section B is different from that which you looked at for Section A. Again, you are presented with texts drawn from the world around you — leaflets, club flyers, transcripts of genuine conversations and extracts from online communication — but here your focus needs to be as much on the contexts that produce the texts and the wider social contexts related to them as it is on the details of the language itself.

Section B questions are assessed using two assessment objectives:

- AO2 (16 marks): concepts and issues related to the topic
- AO3 (32 marks): contextual awareness

The difference between these two AOs in Section B is that AO2 is focused more on your knowledge of theories, case studies and concepts related to the topic, while AO3 relates to your understanding of the specific text you analyse, the language features within it and the context in which it was produced.

The weighting of the AOs is important as AO3 is worth twice as many marks as AO2. In practice — and according to examiners' reports for this course — this means that you should avoid overloading your answer with too much name-dropping of theorists and case studies, and instead look for ways in which your understanding of theory and research can be used to inform your analysis of the texts.

Below is a simplified version of the Section B mark scheme.

**Mark scheme for Section B**

|  | AO2 (16 marks)<br>Concepts and issues related to the topic | AO3 (32 marks)<br>Contextual awareness |
|---|---|---|
| Very good | Sensitive understanding of range of ideas and concepts<br>Conceptualised discussion of ideas<br>Relevant examples from study integrated into discussion | Perceptive and insightful grasp of contextual factors<br>Systematic and analytical focus on language<br>Focused and intelligent use of data in question |
| Sound—good | Some awareness (sound) — clear understanding (good) of language concepts<br>Selection of issues (sound) — range of issues (good)<br>Selecting and exploring relevant examples from study | Some consideration (sound) — clear understanding (good) of contextual factors<br>Awareness (sound) — sound analysis (good) of contextual factors and links to language<br>Uses examples increasingly well |
| Undeveloped | Limited and superficial<br>In need of more depth, range and detail | Too broad or too limited<br>In need of more attention to contexts and/or better use of textual examples |
| Very weak | Weak grasp of language issues<br>Little relevant discussion | Superficial, unsupported and weak |

# Language and gender

## First gender text (AA): interaction and gender

The texts that you are given for language and gender might be in the form of texts that represent gender in some way or those that show gender as a factor in interaction. Of course, gender being such an all-embracing area of language, it is more than likely that the texts chosen will do a bit of both. So, do not be surprised to find a text such as a comic strip in which gender is represented in terms of how males or females are constructed as participants, but also as users of language — perhaps having speech bubbles which reflect ideas about how males and females communicate. It is also quite possible that you will be presented with transcripts (of spoken or online communication) in which the speakers construct gender identities for themselves through the language they use, but also reflect existing ideas about gender relations in their social roles.

Remember that gender is generally regarded as a social construct — not something that we are born with, but something we learn about as we grow older — and that it is only one element of our identities. Many linguists have argued that we 'perform' gender in our language choices, sending out messages about how we see ourselves as members of society. Remember also that while much research has been done on how women speak and how women are represented, gender is about males too.

The following is an extract of a transcript of a conversation between three young men in a pub.

---

**Transcription key**

| | |
|---|---|
| (.) | micropause |
| (1) | pause of number of seconds in brackets |
| <points to ring> | description of non-verbal actions/features |
| [some words] <br> [other words] } | simultaneous speech |
| **bold** | emphatic stress |
| = | latched talk |

---

**A**  When's Darren getting here then

**B**  Err (.) he texted about twenty minutes back (.) he was tryin' to get out of work but his boss was still hangin' around causing trouble

**A**  **That** woman (1) Jeez I can't stand her <laughs>

**C**  You used to work with her didn't you

**A**  Yeah couple of years back at that games shop

**C**  You told me you'd copped off with her at the Christmas party

**B**  You copped off with [your **boss]**

**A**  [Oh man] just leave it

**B**  But you did (1) you copped off with your boss <all laugh>

**A**  Yeah yeah alright (.) just leave it

**C**  How things change

**A**  I never **liked** her though (.) like **liked** her

**B**  That's not what it looked like under the mistletoe (.) by the [fairy lights]

**A**  [**Nooooo**] I **fancied** her then but I never **liked** her that much

**B**  Maybe just a little bit

**A**  **No** not even a little bit

**B**  Not even just a **tiny** bit

**A**  There were **bits** I liked <all laugh>

**B**  You're just a P.I.M.P. <starts singing a 50 Cent song> <all laugh>

**A**  Joe (.) your round innit (.) get us another Stella will you

**C**  Yeah (.) Neil what you havin'

**B**  Same again ta

**A**  What another Malibu and coke

**B**  Very funny

**C**  JD and coke yeah

**1** What would be a good starting point for your analysis of the context of this text? Which factors of context are most important?

........................................................................................................................

........................................................................................................................

........................................................................................................................

........................................................................................................................

**2** Which language methods do you think are most relevant to the analysis of gender issues in this text?

........................................................................................................................

........................................................................................................................

........................................................................................................................

........................................................................................................................

**3** Jennifer Coates in *Men Talk* (2002) makes a number of points about the nature of 'banter' between some males and looks at the ways in which there is often 'verbal jousting' between boys and men, used as a means of 'constructing solidarity' between them. In other words, the humorous abuse helps to bond the men together further. Where do you think there might be evidence in this transcript to support Coates' observations?

........................................................................................................................

........................................................................................................................

........................................................................................................................

**4** Deborah Tannen in her book *You Just Don't Understand* (1992) proposes that males and females have different communicative approaches. She claims that men compete and women cooperate. Can you spot any evidence for that in this extract?

........................................................................................................................

........................................................................................................................

........................................................................................................................

**5** The sociolinguist, Deborah Cameron, in her *Myth of Mars and Venus* (2010), argues that we are too fixated on differences *between* the sexes and should also think about the differences *within* the sexes. Can you see any evidence in this extract for the individual young men communicating in different ways?

........................................................................................................................

........................................................................................................................

........................................................................................................................

........................................................................................................................

## Second gender text (AB): representation and gender

Then Princess Pearl stepped forward, crying, "STOP, you silly chumps!
The world's already far too full of cuts and burns and bumps.
Don't rescue me! I won't go back to being a princess
And prancing round the palace in a silly frilly dress.

"I want to be a doctor, and travel here and there,
Listening to people's chests and giving them my care."

"Me, too!" exclaimed the knight, and took his helmet off his head.
"I'd rather wear a nice twisty stethoscope," he said.

"Perhaps, Princess, you'll train me up?" And Pearl replied, "Of course,
But I don't see how the two of us could fit upon your horse."

*Zog: text © Julia Donaldson, 2010; illustration © Axel Scheffler, 2010; reproduced with the permission of Scholastic Ltd. All rights reserved.*

**6** The language in this extract represents gender in several interesting ways. What would be the most important features to comment on here?

.......................................................................................................................................................

.......................................................................................................................................................

.......................................................................................................................................................

.......................................................................................................................................................

.......................................................................................................................................................

.......................................................................................................................................................

.......................................................................................................................................................

.......................................................................................................................................................

**7** This text is taken from a book aimed at children. How significant do you think the gender representations might be for this target audience?

.......................................................................................................................................................

.......................................................................................................................................................

.......................................................................................................................................................

.......................................................................................................................................................

.......................................................................................................................................................

.......................................................................................................................................................

**8** Which language concepts, case studies and theorists might be relevant to your analysis of a text like this?

.......................................................................................................................................................

.......................................................................................................................................................

.......................................................................................................................................................

.......................................................................................................................................................

.......................................................................................................................................................

# Language and power

When looking at language and power questions you should be thinking about both how power is represented through language and how participants in an interaction position themselves and use strategies to gain power.

In spoken texts you might come across examples of specific word or sentence choices which are designed to exert power over other participants in the transcript. You might also notice a bigger picture, where the context of the transcript is important. In situations like these — classroom, courtroom, police station, office meetings — it is helpful to think about what normally happens in these interactions and how those practices are reflected (or not) in the texts you are analysing.

In written extracts you might come across texts designed to persuade and influence the reader, texts designed to warn or texts designed to offer advice and instruction. Again, small details can be important, but wider strategies such as the ways in which readers are addressed (perhaps using **synthetic personalisation**), how **influential** or **instrumental** power are exercised, and how the reader is positioned in relation to the subject matter being discussed can all be significant.

Many linguists have studied power in written and social discourses, including Norman Fairclough, Deborah Cameron and O'Barr and Atkins, and their ideas and research can be helpful to your understanding of the ways in which power is exercised. Once again though, while these ideas can be helpful, they should not be forced to fit into your answers. Try instead to work with the texts first and then relate what you interpret and analyse from the texts to relevant ideas from language study, rather than the other way round.

## First power text (BA)

The following transcript is an extract of a conversation held in a classroom at the beginning of a Year 8 English lesson between a teacher and his class. The students who speak are A–D.

---

**Transcription key**

| | |
|---|---|
| (.) | micropause |
| (1) | pause of number of seconds in brackets |
| <points to ring> | description of non-verbal actions |
| [some words]<br>[other words] } | simultaneous speech |
| **bold** | emphatic stress |
| = | latched talk |

| | |
|---|---|
| **Teacher** | Can I have some quiet please (1) I'm still waiting (2) still waiting (2) right (.) that's better (.) thank you (1) Ryan (.) when I asked for quiet that applied to you too (.) why are you still talking (.) |
| **A** | I was just = |
| **Teacher** | = You were just about to close your mouth weren't you (.) thank you |
| **A** | Yes sir (.) |
| **Teacher** | OK now where had we got to with *The Hunger Games* (1) Temitope can you tell us please |
| **B** | Err (.) we had read up to the part where she had volunteered instead of her little sister |
| **Teacher** | Yes (.) that's right |
| **C** | Sir (.) I wasn't here last lesson (.) what happened |
| **Teacher** | Niall you can read can't you |
| **C** | Yeah |
| **Teacher** | So read it yourself if you miss a lesson (.) we can't read it for you |
| **Class** | <laughter> |
| **Teacher** | OK settle down now please (.) Ryan (.) why are you fiddling in your bag |
| **D** | It's his Blackberry [sir] |
| **A** | [**Snitch**] |
| **D** | But it is |
| **A** | No it aint |
| **Teacher** | Listen (.) the two of you (.) **Listen** (.) this is unacceptable (.) Ryan turn off your phone and put it in your bag = |
| **A** | = It is off I was just turning it off = |
| **Teacher** | = and take your bag and yourself to Miss Henry's room where you can explain to her how you have wasted all our time this morning |
| **A** | **Sirrrr** (.) I'm sorry (.) it won't happen again |
| **Teacher** | You're right about that (1) off you pop (.) to Miss Henry's classroom please (2) I'm waiting (1) thank you (2) now back to the book |

---

**1** **The classroom context is important to the interaction seen in this text. What impact does the classroom setting have on the participants and the language they use?**

**2** In terms of specific language features, how does the teacher exercise power and control over the class?

....................................................................................................

....................................................................................................

....................................................................................................

....................................................................................................

....................................................................................................

....................................................................................................

**3** Linguists who have studied power and discourse make a number of points about patterns that we see in *asymmetrical* exchanges like this. Which language concepts and theories that you have studied would be relevant to what happens in this transcript?

....................................................................................................

....................................................................................................

....................................................................................................

....................................................................................................

....................................................................................................

....................................................................................................

....................................................................................................

## Second power text (BB)

This text is taken from the footer of an e-mail message sent out by a teacher at a sixth form college. It is the standard message that is applied to all e-mails that come from that college.

### Sir Andrew Eldritch College

The contents of all email and any attachments are strictly private and confidential and may contain information which is subject to legal privilege. Such email may not be used or disclosed under any circumstances by anyone who is not a named recipient. Please return the email if you are not the intended or named recipient. Unauthorised use of the email or its contents is prohibited and may be unlawful. Incoming and outgoing email is subject to continuous and ad hoc filtering, scrutiny and reporting.

The college accepts no liability whatsoever for any damage, loss or expense arising from this email and/or from the accessing of any files attached to this email. This email may not necessarily reflect the views or intentions of Sir Andrew Eldritch College or its governing body, who therefore do not accept any liability whatsoever for any claims, loss or damages of whatsoever nature, arising directly or indirectly, as a result of the reliance on such information by anyone. Unless the intention to contract has been expressly manifested in this message by a duly authorised representative of the college, this message shall not be construed as a solicitation to contract nor an offer or acceptance of any contractual obligations.

The addressee's address will not be disclosed to others for commercial intent.

Please notify the college should you not wish to receive email from the college.

**4** In what ways is power exerted on the reader of this e-mail message? Point to specific examples where possible.

.............................................................................................................................

.............................................................................................................................

.............................................................................................................................

.............................................................................................................................

.............................................................................................................................

**5** Which language methods are most useful for analysing the language of this text? Choose three examples of language use and say which methods could work best with them.

.............................................................................................................................

.............................................................................................................................

.............................................................................................................................

.............................................................................................................................

.............................................................................................................................

# Language and technology

You are expected to be aware of how technologies shape the way people communicate — the affordances and constraints of technologies such as text messaging, MSN, telephone conversations or voice over internet protocol (VOIP) — and also the social practices connected to the technologies and how these are demonstrated in the language and structure of the extracts.

It is quite common to find exam texts which have online or telephone conversations and it is perfectly acceptable (encouraged even) to apply your skills of spoken and written language analysis from Section A to texts in this section, as long as you are aware of how other areas might also apply.

In terms of wider theoretical concepts and understanding of language issues, it is helpful to be able to apply your knowledge of how linguists and other researchers have studied these forms of communication and how their findings might impact on the data you are analysing. For example, work by researchers like Sali Tagliamonte, Mike Thelwall and Angela Goddard on instant messaging, social networking and online identity creation respectively might help you make sense of a technology text.

Once again though, it is important to be driven by the data rather than the theory, so you should start with the text you are presented with and the context it has been produced in, rather than trying to apply the theory you have learned first.

## First technology text (CA)

Text CA is taken from the web forum of a rock festival. The participants are posting their views on the festival that has just finished.

| User 1 | Post subject: Well what did you think? | Posted  Monday June 13 2011: 6.40am |
|---|---|---|
| | Well? Opinions pleeeease... | |

| User 2 | Post subject: Well what did you think? | Posted  Monday June 13 2011: 6.42am |
|---|---|---|
| | my thoughts – 2 many people in dance tent – 2 many chavs and underage idiots at beer tents and to much rain!!! apart from that it was as good as last years festie | |

| User 3 | Post subject: Well what did you think? | Posted  Monday June 13 2011: 6.43am |
|---|---|---|
| | good points - | |
| | metronymy | |
| | the walkmen | |
| | death cab | |
| | the national | |
| | security not finding my hipflask | |
| | the girl with the pink hat at the woodland beer tent ♥ ♥ ♥ ♥ ♥ | |
| | | |
| | bad points - | |
| | rain | |
| | enter shikari (why?) | |
| | rain | |
| | the vaccines | |
| | rain | |
| | the couple in the next tent who "kissed" loudly all night (urgh) 🙂 | |
| | did i mention the rain? | |

| User 4 | Post subject: Well what did you think? | Posted  Monday June 13 2011: 6.45am |
|---|---|---|

> | User 3 | Post subject: Well what did you think? | Posted  Monday June 13 2011: 6.43am |
> |---|---|---|
> | | good points – | |
> | | the national | |

this

> | User 3 | Post subject: Well what did you think? | Posted  Monday June 13 2011: 6.43am |
> |---|---|---|
> | | bad points – | |
> | | the vaccines | |

this

| User 1 | Post subject: Well what did you think? | Posted  Monday June 13 2011: 6.47am |
|---|---|---|
| | Really have no idea why people hate the Vaccines so much. FWIW I thought they were one of the highlights of weekend. | |

| User 4 | Post subject: Well what did you think? | Posted  Monday June 13 2011: 6.49am |
|---|---|---|

> | User 1 | Post subject: Well what did you think? | Posted  Monday June 13 2011: 6.47am |
> |---|---|---|
> | | Really have no idea why people hate the Vaccines so much. FWIW I thought they were one of the highlights of weekend. | |

ova-hyped fake indie. but your entitled to an opinion

| User 1 | Post subject: Well what did you think? | Posted  Monday June 13 2011: 6.50am |
|---|---|---|

> | User 4 | Post subject: Well what did you think? | Posted  Monday June 13 2011: 6.49am |
> |---|---|---|
> 
> > | User 1 | Post subject: Well what did you think? | Posted  Monday June 13 2011: 6.47am |
> > |---|---|---|
> > | | Really have no idea why people hate the Vaccines so much. FWIW I thought they were one of the highlights of weekend. | |
> 
> ova-hyped fake indie. but your entitled to an opinion

That's big of you. Thanks.

37

Text CA is fairly typical of many discussion forums where a topic is introduced by one poster and then others respond. Extracts like this do not necessarily involve interaction, because sometimes the individual posters will just put their own opinions forward with no reference to what others before them have said, but in this text there is some clear interaction taking place.

**1** **Where is there evidence of interaction between posters in this text and how can you tell?**

.............................................................................................................................

.............................................................................................................................

.............................................................................................................................

**2** **Many forms of computer-mediated communication (CMC) display evidence of non-standard language use, be it in punctuation, abbreviation, spelling, grammar or graphological features such as emoticons. What non-standard language features can you identify in this text and why might they have occurred?**

.............................................................................................................................

.............................................................................................................................

.............................................................................................................................

.............................................................................................................................

**3** **Not everyone has the same individual style of language (idiolect) in speech, writing or CMC. Examiners are often keen to reward candidates who can see differences between individual participants. What evidence can you find for different participants in this interaction having distinct idiolects?**

.............................................................................................................................

.............................................................................................................................

.............................................................................................................................

**4** **Studies of some CMC have indicated that participants often exhibit different types of behaviour online when they think they are anonymous than they would adopt in a face-to-face conversation. Identify examples of where this might be the case in text CA and how language has been used in a way that you think is worthy of further comment.**

.............................................................................................................................

.............................................................................................................................

.............................................................................................................................

**5** **This exchange is made possible by a form of CMC. What makes this 'conversation' different from a genuine spoken conversation?**

.............................................................................................................................

.............................................................................................................................

.............................................................................................................................

.............................................................................................................................

# Second technology text (CB)

This text is a screen shot of the home page of the English and Media Centre's publications page.
http://www.englishandmedia.co.uk/publications/index.php

*Reproduced by permission of the English and Media Centre*

**6** In what ways has this homepage been designed to be interactive with its readers and users?

.....................................................................................................................................

.....................................................................................................................................

.....................................................................................................................................

.....................................................................................................................................

.....................................................................................................................................

**7** What kinds of purposes and audiences do you think the homepage is designed for?

.....................................................................................................................................

.....................................................................................................................................

.....................................................................................................................................

.....................................................................................................................................

.....................................................................................................................................

**8** In what ways has the language used on this page been shaped by the fact that it is online?

.....................................................................................................................................

.....................................................................................................................................

.....................................................................................................................................

.....................................................................................................................................

In the pages that follow there are two further examples of texts from each part of Section B: language and gender; language and power; language and technology. Each text is followed by an essay-style question and space to plan your answer. Once you have planned each response, you can write your answer on a separate sheet of paper and check it against the feedback and suggestions available in the online answers.

## Exam-style questions: language and gender

### Text AC: fridge magnets (gender)

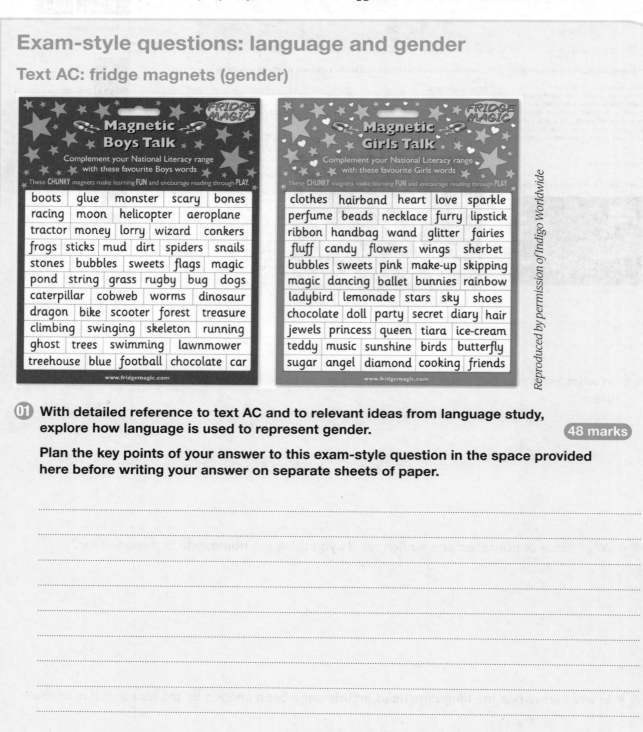

*Reproduced by permission of Indigo Worldwide*

**01** With detailed reference to text AC and to relevant ideas from language study, explore how language is used to represent gender.

**48 marks**

Plan the key points of your answer to this exam-style question in the space provided here before writing your answer on separate sheets of paper.

**Text AD: Fawcett Society poster**

*Reproduced by permission of The Fawcett Society.*

02  With detailed reference to text AD and to relevant ideas from language study, explore how language is used to represent gender.  **48 marks**

Plan the key points of your answer to this exam-style question in the space provided here before writing your answer on separate sheets of paper.

## How your gift can help someone who is struggling and alone

This Christmas we aim to offer all of these services and more – but we depend on your support now.

- Hot, delicious, nutritious Christmas dinners for 2,800 homeless people over eight days
- Advice on housing, benefits, finances, employment, immigration/asylum, as well as legal matters
- Healthcare including TB and hepatitis screenings
- Dental treatment and eye tests, including reading glasses
- Hairdressing and massage
- Learning and skills opportunities, internet cafés and IT workshops
- Specialist centres providing safe accommodation to rough sleepers, women and people with dependency issues

By offering advice and linking people to ongoing services, Crisis at Christmas marks the beginning of year round help and opportunities for homeless people.

### Please give someone like Rob a second chance this Christmas

After his father and two siblings died, Rob spiralled into despair and turned to drink and drugs. His marriage broke down and he lost his home and job. Despite beating his dependency, Rob ended up sleeping rough. Rob decided to approach Crisis and has since been rehoused. Crisis Employment Services also helped Rob seek work. He volunteered for Crisis at Christmas and Crisis Skylight, which helps homeless people learn new skills. **'Till the day I die I'll bend over backwards to help because Crisis pushed me in the right direction.' Rob**

### 40 years of saving lives

Crisis at Christmas has provided vital services for homeless people for 40 years. Whilst we celebrate the lives changed, we need your help more than ever to end homelessness so that one day we are not needed at all.

Crisis
at Christmas
Changing Lives
for 40 Years

This Ch

A lifeline

## This Christmas, throw someone in crisis a lifeline

For someone who is homeless, a Crisis at Christmas dinner offers so much more than just one hot meal. It can offer a whole new beginning.

It can lead to anything from a new set of clothes, a haircut and a dental treatment to education, employment and housing advice.

For each person who comes to Crisis for Christmas dinner, it can be a chance to receive the one thing they need most to begin to turn their lives around.

CRISIS

# CRISIS

### ...as dinner saves lives

#### ...hn

...John was four his brother was killed in the Second World War
...bing. Unable to cope with the tragedy, his father committed suicide.
...n's mother remarried three years later, but her new husband was an
...oholic and would violently abuse her and the children.

...e age of 14, frightened for his mother's safety, John hit his
...ather over the head with a chair. John and his younger brother
...then taken into care. Soon after, John's younger brother died of
...mia and his mother drowned herself.

When he was 18, John found work as a cocktail waiter in hotel
bars. But he was often forced to sleep rough between jobs.
Incredibly lonely and terrified of arrest, at night he would
lie grasping his most precious possession to his chest:
a picture of himself with his mother. After suffering a
nervous breakdown, John spent time in an institute for
mentally ill people.

Now retired, John rents a room in a lodging house
for formerly homeless men. 'I've come to Crisis
at Christmas for the wonderful hospitality,
efficient transport, delicious food and kindness
of the volunteers,' he says.

**Support Crisis at Christmas 2011
and throw someone a lifeline.**

Complete your form now or call
08000 199 099 to find out more.

# Exam-style questions: language and power

## Text BC: Crisis charity leaflet

**03** **With detailed reference to text BC and
to relevant ideas from language study,
explore how written language is used
to persuade.** **48 marks**

**Plan the key points of your answer to this
exam-style question in the space provided here
before writing your answer on separate sheets
of paper.**

...........................................................................................

...........................................................................................

...........................................................................................

...........................................................................................

...........................................................................................

...........................................................................................

...........................................................................................

...........................................................................................

...........................................................................................

...........................................................................................

...........................................................................................

...........................................................................................

...........................................................................................

...........................................................................................

...........................................................................................

...........................................................................................

...........................................................................................

...........................................................................................

...........................................................................................

...........................................................................................

...........................................................................................

...........................................................................................

...........................................................................................

**The following text is a letter sent to London residents by the Mayor of London, Boris Johnson.**

Dear Ms Egerton,

Badly managed roadworks are a headache for Londoners and a drain on our economy.

I have just introduced new, tighter standards for roadworks and making it easier for you to tell us when you spot sloppy examples so we can take action to sort it out. You can report sites that don't come up to scratch at **tfl.gov.uk/roadworks**

TfL has pledged that all its roadworks will meet these standards. Any other organisation working on TfL's roads will be monitored using CCTV and traffic police community support officers.

Most roads in London are managed by local boroughs, so I'm asking them to meet the standards too. Your reports will be passed directly to the relevant authority, and my team will work to ensure improvements are made.

We are getting laws put in place by next year that allow us to properly charge for working on our roads — creating a real incentive to do works with minimum disruption.

In the meantime, thank you for your help in keeping London moving.

Yours sincerely,

Boris Johnson

Mayor of London and Chairman of Transport for London

**Source:** http://www.london.gov.uk/media/press_releases_mayoral/mayor-tightens-grip-disruptive-roadworks-london)

**04** **With detailed reference to text BD and to relevant ideas from language study, explore how written language is used to express power.** **48 marks**

**Plan the key points of your answer to this exam-style question in the space provided here before writing your answer on separate sheets of paper.**

# Exam-style questions: language and technology

## Text CC

**Text CC is an extract from a telephone call made to a customer services centre. AV is the automated voice and CSR is the customer service representative. The caller is C.**

| Transcription key | |
|---|---|
| (.) | micropause |
| (1) | pause of number of seconds in bracket |
| [points to ring] | description of non-verbal actions |
| **bold** | emphatic stress |
| = | latched talk |

**AV**  Hello and welcome to the SBS Customer Service centre (.) all calls may be recorded for training purposes (1) in a moment we will give you four options to choose from (.) at any point you can press star to return to the main menu (.) OK (.) if you would like to report your card lost or stolen please press 1 (.) if you would like to make a balance transfer press 2 (.) if you would like to make a payment press 3 (.) or for any other enquiry just press 4

[Caller presses 4]

**AV**  OK (.) if you would like to inform us of a change of address press 1 (.) if you would like to ask about increasing your credit limit please press (2) or for any other enquiry please press 3

[Caller presses 3]

**AV**  Thanks (.) we will now transfer you to a customer service representative (.) please bear with us as it sometimes takes a moment to connect (3) have you heard about our new Platinum awards card (.) for a competitive 10.9% APR you can have all the benefits of your normal SBS card with the added bonus of monthly cashback on everything you spend (.) just ask a customer service representative for more details (1) transferring

**CSR**  Hello and welcome to the SBS Customer Service centre my name is Lynn may I take your name please

**C**  It's Mr J Tweedy

**CSR**  Thank you Mr Tweedy (.) now may I have your card number and card expiry date please

**C**  The card number is 492900010002 (.) and the expiry date is err (.) 02 14

**CSR**  Thank you (1) that's all fine (.) and how may I help you today

**C**  Erm (.) I'd like to query an item on my err bill (.) last month's statement please

**CSR**  Of course (.) and for what amount was this transaction

**C**  Err (.) £69.99 I think (1) hang on a minute (.) just have to check (2) yes (.) it was £69.99 on the 3rd of May

**CSR**  Thank you (1) I can see a transaction for that amount on the 3rd of May (.) payable to Votal Financial Services (.) what is it that you'd like to query about this transaction

**C**  Well it shouldn't have gone out (.) I sold the car the month before and that payment was for a service agreement which I no longer need (.) I spoke to the garage and they said I wouldn't need to cancel it (.) cos they would just handle it at their end (.) but (.) err it looks like they're still taking the money

**CSR**  I see yes (.) I'm afraid there's nothing I can do at this end Mr Tweedy (.) you will need to take the matter up with Votal Financial Services and seek a refund for the outstanding money from them (.) I can only action suspected fraudulent transactions or transactions that take the cardholder over the agreed credit limit (1)

**C**  Oh I see (.) OK

**CSR**  is there anything else I can help you with today Mr Tweedy

**C**  No that's OK (.) thanks

**CSR**  Thank you for your call (.) goodbye

**05** With detailed reference to text CC and to relevant ideas from language study, explore how technology affects language use.

48 marks

Think about details from the text and how they relate to the wider influences of technology on language.

## Text CD

**Text CD is an extract from a Twitter timeline.**

| | | |
|---|---|---|
| **Radio Indie** @Radioindie | | 4m |
| #nowplaying The Shins Simple Song | | |

**Radio Indie** @Radioindie — 4m
#nowplaying The Shins Simple Song

**Yorkshirewhite** @LUFC4EVA — 13m
Ken Bates has resigned! Leeds United is safe once more! #LUFC #batesout
Retweeted by LeedsLeedsLeeds

**Chris** @christophe — 14m
Some things that you might like to eat here http://www.madeupwebaddress.com

**LeedsLeedsLeeds** @L33d5 — 16m
Can this really b tru??? Bates is resigning!! please make this true

**RedRobbo** @redrobborobsdarich — 19m
If you hate Tory cuts to disabled benefits sign this http://www.madeupepetition.com
Retweeted by WalthamForestAntiCuts

**Smog Festival** @smogfest2012 — 19m
First bands announced for SmogFest 2012. Midlake, John Grant, Antlers, Suuns...and some xtra special guests. We're excited are you? More coming.

---

**06** With detailed reference to text CD and to relevant ideas from language study, explore how technology affects language use.

**48 marks**

Think about details from the text and how they relate to the wider influences of technology on language.

Plan the key points of your answer to this exam-style question in the space provided here before writing your answer on separate sheets of paper.

Continue writing on the next page.

# Summary

If you want to succeed in this examination you need to show that you can analyse language, understand why language is used in different ways in different situations and demonstrate understanding of key language concepts.

## Section A Text varieties

- Examiners like to see students who can think on their feet, so do not try to reproduce a pre-prepared answer or even pre-prepared groupings.
- Think of a good range of groups, using more than just purpose and language groupings. Think about multi-modal texts, genre, audience, humour and whatever else strikes you. Examiners reward originality.
- Think about which texts might appear in more than one group and explain how this can happen.
- Be aware of differences within groups and be prepared to describe subtle variations using a comparative vocabulary that reflects careful consideration of this.
- Always try to link language features to contextual features. Avoid just spotting and labelling features.
- Be linguistic. This is an English Language paper, so use appropriate terminology and show what you have learned.

- Signpost your groups clearly. Tell the examiner which groupings you have made and the texts that are within them.

## Section B Language and social contexts

- Show that you have studied English Language for a year by writing in a linguistic and precise register.
- Do not just offload as much knowledge as you can from your head onto the page. Think about the most relevant points that might apply to the questions set.
- Think about context. Texts are not produced in a vacuum: they will have various reasons for existing and various purposes to serve and audiences to address, so you need to show awareness of these factors.
- Use language terminology accurately, but do not try to feature spot everything you can recognise. Discussing language features is important but you also need to discuss how they are used and what effects they create.

Philip Allan, an imprint of Hodder Education, an Hachette UK company, Market Place, Deddington, Oxfordshire, OX15 0SE

*Orders*
Bookpoint Ltd, 130 Milton Park, Abingdon, Oxfordshire OX14 4SB
tel: 01235 827827   fax: 01235 400401
e-mail: education@bookpoint.co.uk
Lines are open 9.00 a.m.–5.00 p.m., Monday to Saturday, with a 24-hour message answering service. You can also order through the Philip Allan website: **www.philipallan.co.uk**

© Dan Clayton 2012
ISBN 978-1-4441-6455-8
First printed 2012
Impression number 5    4    3    2
Year 2017       2016 2015 2014 2013 2012

Printed in Dubai

Hachette UK's policy is to use papers that are natural, renewable and recyclable products and made from wood grown in sustainable forests. The logging and manufacturing processes are expected to conform to the environmental regulations of the country of origin.
P02119

www.philipallan.co.uk

ISBN 978-1-4441-6455-8